[W]elcome to the latest VIZ graphic novel sampler, a sneak peek [i]nto 9 brand-new manga from VIZ.

These are some of the most exciting, funniest, romantic, thought-provoking, and hottest manga to launch from Japan to North America this Fall!

VIZ MANGA MEANS VIZ QUALITY!

• The best, most appealing, and unique titles!

• English adaptations that seamlessly bridge the gap between Japanese and English to bring out the subtleties of the dialogue and each character!

• Artful lettering and sound effects uniquely honed to suit the original artwork!

• High-quality reproduction so you don't miss a *single line* of the artist's original artwork!

Go ahead, flip through this book and sample a title or two for FREE…and remember, there's more where this came from!

Manga SneakPeek 2004
CONTENTS

DOLLS
Story & Art **Yumiko Kawahara**
English Adaptation **Kaori Inoue**
Touch-Up Art & Lettering **Gia Cam Luc**
Cover & Interior Design **Izumi Evers**
Editor **Eric Searleman**
© Yumiko Kawahara. Originally published in Japan in 2001 by Asahi SONORAMA Co., Ltd., Tokyo. English translation rights arranged with Asahi SONORAMA Co., Ltd.

FROM FAR AWAY
Story & Art **Kyoko Hikawa**
English Adaptation **Trina Robbins**
Touch-Up Art & Lettering **Walden Wong**
Cover & Interior Design **Carolina Ugalde**
Editor **Eric Searleman**
Kanatakara by Kyoko Hikawa © Kyoko Hikawa 1991. All rights reserved. First published in Japan in 1992 by HAKUSENSHA, Inc., Tokyo. English language translation rights in America and Canada arranged with HAKUSENSHA, Inc., Tokyo.

HERE IS GREENWOOD
Story & Art **Yukie Nasu**
English Adaptation **William Flanagan**
Touch-Up Art & Lettering **Walden Wong**
Cover & Interior Design **Hidemi Sahara**
Editor **Michelle Pangilinan**
Koko wa Greenwood by Yukie Nasu © Yukie Nasu 1986. All rights reserved. First published in Japan in 1996 by HAKUSENSHA, Inc., Tokyo. English language translation rights in America and Canada arranged with HAKUSENSHA, Inc., Tokyo.

NO NEED FOR TENCHI!
THE GRAPHIC NOVEL EDITION
Story & Art **Hitoshi Okuda**
English Adaptation **Fred Burke**
Touch-Up Art & Lettering **Mark McMurray**
Cover & Interior Design **Sean Lee**
Editor **Shaenon K. Garrity**
© HITOSHI OKUDA 1994 © AIC/VAP•NTV. Originally published in Japan in 1994 by KADOKAWA SHOTEN PUBLISHING CO, LTD, Tokyo. English translation rights arranged with KADOKAWA SHOTEN PUBLISHING CO, LTD, Tokyo.

REVOLUTIONARY GIRL UTENA:
THE ADOLESCENCE OF UTENA
Story & Art **Chiho Saito**
Created **Be-PaPas**
English Adaptation **Fred Burke**
Touch-Up Art & Lettering **Steve Dutro**
Cover & Interior Design **Carolina Ugalde**
Editor **Eric Searleman**
© 1996 SAITO CHIHO/ BE-PAPAS/Shogakukan. First published by Shogakukan, Inc. in Japan as "Shojo Kakumei Utena, Gekijoban Adouresensu Mokujiroku."

TOUGH
Story & Art **Tetsuya Saruwatari**
English Adaptation **Lance Caselman**
Touch-Up Art & Lettering **Gabe Crate**
Cover & Interior Design **Izumi Evers**
Editor **Yuki Takagaki**
KOKO TEKKEN-DEN TOUGH ©1993 by TETSUYA SARUWATARI. All rights reserved. First published in Japan in 1993 by SHUEISHA Inc., Tokyo. English translation rights in the United States of America and Canada arranged by SHUEISHA Inc. through CLOVERWAY INC.

WILD COM.
Story & Art **Yumi Tamura**
English Adaptation **Gerard Jones**
Touch-Up Art & Lettering **Steve Dutro**
Cover & Interior Design **Carolina Ugalde**
Editor **P. Duffield**
© 1999 Yumi Tamura/Shogakukan, Inc. First published by Shogakukan, Inc. in Japan as "Super Natural Powers Wild Com."

W JULIET
Story & Art **Emura**
English Adaptation **William Flanagan**
Touch-Up Art & Lettering **Mark McMurray**
Cover & Interior Design **Hidemi Sahara**
Editor **Megan Bates**
W Juliet by Emura © Emura 1997 All rights reserved. First published in Japan in 1999 by HAKUSENSHA, Inc., Tokyo. English language translation rights in America and Canada arranged with HAKUSENSHA, Inc., Tokyo.

WOLF'S RAIN
Story **BONES, Keiko Nobumoto**
Art **Toshitsugu Iida**
English Adaptation **David Ury/Egan Loo**
Special Thanks **David Fleming**
Touch-up Art & Lettering **Gia Cam Luc**
Cover & Interior Design **Veronica Casson**
Editor **Egan Loo**
© 2003 TOSHITSUGU IIDA and BONES• KEIKO NOBUMO-TO/BV. All rights reserved. First published in Japan in 2003 by Kodansha, Ltd., Tokyo. English translation rights arranged through Kodansha Ltd.

shôjo

shô•jo (sho′jo) *n.* **1.** Manga appealing to both female and male readers. **2.** Exciting stories with true-to-life characters and the thrill of exotic locales. **3.** Connecting the heart and mind through real human relationships.

Shôjo titles from VIZ:

**Dolls • From Far Away • Here is Greenwood •
Revolutionary Girl Utena: The Adolescence of Utena •
Wild Com. • W Juliet**

THIS ONE IS QUITE MILD MANNERED AND LIKES TO BE TIDY.

OH, NOT AT ALL.

THANK YOU VERY MUCH, SIR.

Just what are you?

If you would like, I can also sign it for you.

YOU'RE GOOD AT DRAWING.

WHAT ARE YOUR THOUGHTS, SIR?

...ISN'T THE CARE PRETTY DIFFI-CULT?

BUT... WELL...

IF YOU PURCHASE NOW, I WILL THROW IN A REPLICA OF A JUMEAU DOLL'S DRESS.

Looks like this.

JUMEAU: FAMOUS FRENCH DOLL MAKER.

FOR FEED-INGS, YOU NEED ONLY TO PROVIDE MILK THREE TIMES A DAY.

THAT'S IT?

WE ALSO STOCK THIS VERY CONVEN-IENT COMPOUND FERTILIZER THAT IS LADEN WITH VITAMINS AND MINERALS.

ALL THAT IS LEFT IS TO FEED IT SUGAR COOKIES AS A FERTILIZER APPROXIMATELY ONCE A WEEK TO MAINTAIN A HEALTHY GLOW.

WHAT SHOULD I DO?

CARING FOR A PLANT DOLL...

WELL, LET ME THINK...

THE *MASTER* RAISED HER IN THE LAP OF LUXURY SO...

SHE JUST WON'T DRINK ANY MILK.

IT MIGHT BE FUTILE IF YOUR CUP IS OF A CHEAP QUALITY.

...

A CUP LIKE THIS HAPPENS TO BE AVAILABLE FOR PURCHASE...

I would be happy to place an order

THE OTHER DAY WHEN I INQUIRED WITH THE MASTER, HE REVEALED HE HAD USED A VERY SELECT TYPE OF MILK...

THAT WOULD ENTIRELY DEPEND ON HOW YOU RAISE HER.

Receipt.
Consultation: first payment received.

IT IS ONE OF THE GREAT CHARMS OF A PLANT DOLL.

COULD SHE... LEARN TO DO TRICKS?

TRICKS, YOU SAY?

YOU KNOW, LIKE SING OR DANCE?

THAT'S RIGHT.

I SAW AN "ANGEL" IN THE LITTLE GIRL.

HAVE HER LISTEN TO MUSIC.

SHOW HER VIDEOS.

THE "ANGEL"...

LICKS MILK THREE TIMES A DAY, PLAYS WITH DOLLS...

OCCASIONALLY SHE GAZES TOWARDS ME...

AND SMILES HER ENIGMATIC SMILE.

AND SLEEPS NESTLED IN SILK SHEETS.

I START SHOWING A BIT OF MY MISCHIEVOUS SIDE.

MEAT, FISH, CURRY.

NATTO.

RICE.

Smellier.

Smelly, hm?

Even smellier still.

WHIP

Shake shake shake

THUS MY DAYS ARE NOW SPENT WORKING TO SUPPORT THIS MONSTER OF A "WOMAN" INTO WHICH SHE HAS TRANSFORMED.

WHAT ELSE CAN I DO? IT'S MY OWN DOING.

I HAVE TO TAKE RESPONSIBILITY.

...YES... RESPONSIBILITY...

THE END

MAYBE...

TMP
TMP
TMP
TMP

WOW, BEAUTIFUL AND ACCOMPLISHED!

SHE'S ABOUT AS TALL AS YOU ARE, ISN'T SHE?

175cm (5'9")

NICE TO MEET YOU ALL.

SHE WAS A DRAMA CLUB MEMBER AT HER LAST SCHOOL.

AMANO-SAN JUST TRANSFERRED IN.

OOOH!

HW OOM OM

I HAVE A QUESTION!!

HOW TALL ARE YOU?

YOUR SKIN'S SO WHITE! IS THAT MAKEUP?

IS YOUR HAIR REAL? DO YOU HAVE EXTENSIONS?

DO YOU HAVE A BOYFRIEND?!

CHATTR

CHATTR

CHATTR

SO EVERYONE, MAKE FRIENDS WITH HER!

DON'T SWARM AROUND A PRECIOUS NEW CLUB MEMBER!

I'LL GIVE HER THE TOUR! YOU GUYS GET TO WORK ON YOUR EXERCISES!

KYAAAH!

IT'S MIURA-SEMPAI!

!

JUST DO IT!

AWW! NO WAY!

ARRRRGH!!

JUST HOLD IT THERE!

IT'S LIKE THEY'RE GOING TO STRIP HER DOWN TO NOTHING.

SCARY!

MAN, THOSE GIRLS CAN INTERROGATE!

I'D LIKE TO SEE THAT!

31

UM...

I KNOW YOU'RE NOT PREPARED...

...BUT JUST FIND AN OPEN LOCKER, AND YOU CAN MOVE IN.

THANKS FOR BACK THERE...

? THAT'S A WEIRD THING TO ASK.

SORRY, ALL THE GIRLS ARE LIKE THAT.

SO THEY *WERE* BOTHERING YOU.

YEAH.

HEH HEH

THE GIRLS? YOU MEAN ALL GIRLS ARE LIKE THAT?!

AH!

KACHIK

...BUT SOME ARE BETTER AND SOME WORSE.

OUR GIRLS ARE A LITTLE EX-TREME...

BAM

BAM

SO COOL! ♥ KYAAA! TAKE ME AWAY, TOO!

KYAA!

HEY! NO FAIR, HOLDING HANDS!

KYAA!

KYAA!

KYAA!

SHUT-UP!

OH!

IT'S A LITTLE MESSY...

BUT THIS IS THE GIRL'S DRESSING ROOM.

THE GUYS ARE NEXT DOOR.

TO ME, IT HARDLY SEEMED TO TAKE ANY TIME FOR US TO BECOME FRIENDS.

OUR PHYSICAL TYPES ARE THE EXACT OPPOSITE...

...BUT MAKOTO AND I ARE REALLY COMPATIBLE!

BECAUSE YOU SEEM LIKE A GUY AT HEART.

YOU GOT IT! HOW CAN YOU TELL?

RIGHT... YOU HATE IT TOO?

AND YOU HATE THAT BAGGY SOCKS FAD, RIGHT?

AND YOU'RE NOT UP ON FASHION, ARE YOU?

DON'T LET IT BOTHER YOU!

NO.

...♡

WHOA!

AND...

...SHE BOASTS A BRIGHT, POWERFUL APTITUDE FOR DRAMA!

THE ENTIRE CLUB FELT A TANGIBLE TALENT IN HER THAT COULD PLAY ANY PART.

WHEN ON THE STAGE, SHE'S A COMPLETELY DIFFERENT PERSON.

HEE
HEE

IS SHE A NEW MEMBER?

HMM. SHE HAS *SOME* TALENT.

BUT WHAT A SHAME FOR ALL THAT EXAGGERATED PRAISE TO FILL HER HEAD.

Ho Ho!

JIIK

SHE'S A PRO! A PRO!

CHATTR

TELL THE TEACHER THAT WE'VE GOT OUR JULIET...

...TO PLAY THE CULTURAL FESTIVAL!

I JUST ASKED HER TO READ A LITTLE OF THE SCRIPT!

THAT WAS PERFORMANCE QUALITY!

WOW!

...

CHATTR

Romeo + Juliet

CHATTR

...

CHATTR

TRUE. SHE SURE *LOOKS* THE PART.

YOU *FINALLY* SHOW UP, YOUNG LADY?

IF YOU'RE A PART OF THE CLUB, *BE A PART* OF THE CLUB!

THWAK

HO--

OOOH HO HO

HER TALENT DOESN'T HOLD A CANDLE TO ME!

BECAUSE ONLY I CAN POSSIBLY PLAY JULIET!

HO HO

DIDN'T YOU QUIT?

WHAT HAVE I GOTTEN INTO?

YOU'RE THE ONE WHO SAID SHE WANTED TO BE IN PLAYS!

IF YOU WANT TO QUIT, THEN QUIT!

HOW HORRIBLE! HOW CAN A TEACHER BE SO SAVAGE?

TSUGUMI-SEMPAI? YOU WANT TO ACT IN THE PLAY?

HO

WHO'S THAT?

HO

TSUGUMI-SEMPAI. A THIRD-YEAR STUDENT "PRINCESS" WITH AN INCH-THICK SKULL!

HUSSH

↑ Can't stand her.

36

BUT YOU LOOK BETTER THAN ANY OF THE GUYS DO!

AND YOU DOING ROMEO'S DIALOG WILL BE JUST DREAMY!

Dead Slang

I PLAYED A GUY'S PART LAST TIME!

MORE THAN THAT! ALL THE PARTS I'VE PLAYED HAVE BEEN MEN!

...AND ITO-KUN, YOU'RE MY ROMEO! THAT'S AN ORDER!

NOW! WE'LL BE DOING ROMEO AND JULIET...

ZWOING

SHE'LL NEED MAKE-UP.

THE TEACHER IS TOO MUCH OF A TAKARAZUKA FAN.

BUT... SHE'S A GIRL.

YOUR HANDSOME FACE, YOUR SLENDER BODY, YOUR HUSKY VOICE, YOUR WIDE SHOULDERS...

...YOU'RE A CLASSIC LEADING MAN! WONDERFUL!

CAN I RUN AWAY NOW?

WH-WHAT'S WITH THE SUDDEN DECISION?!

ROMEO?

MY PART IS ALWAYS DECIDED THIS WAY!

NOT ON MY TALENT, HUH?

DIIIING

DOOONG

DIIIING

DOOONG

I WANTED TO SEE AMANO-SAN TRY.

EH?

AH!

JULIET ISN'T SET YET.

...WE'LL CHOOSE THE REST OF THE CAST BY TRY-OUT.

NOW THAT THAT'S DECIDED...

OKAY!

HO HO HO!

THIS MEANS I CAN PLAY MY PART WITH ITO-KUN, RIGHT?

MAKOTO TOLD ME THAT SHE WAS IN AN ACCIDENT AS A CHILD, AND IT'S LEFT HER BACK TERRIBLY SCARRED.

SHE ALWAYS CHANGES CLOTHES ALONE.

A GOOD-LOOKING COUPLE!

SURE!

LET'S HEAD ON HOME.

YEAH. YOU COULD SAY THAT.

HUH? MIURA? ARE YOU WAITING FOR SOMEBODY?

PLIP PLIP PLIP

SORRY FOR THE WAIT, ITO-SAN!

BLINK

THAT SHOULD BE BASICALLY A NORMAL THING!

IT'S SO WEIRD FOR ME TO BECOME GOOD FRIENDS WITH A GIRL!

IT'S SOMETHING THAT'S JUST BETWEEN US.

THE REST OF HER IS SO PRETTY!

IT MUST HAVE BEEN HARD ON HER.

MAKOTO IS SO NATURAL!

THEY FORCED ME INTO TRAINING, TOO.

A KARATE DOJO, BUT IT'S NOT VERY SUCCESS-FUL.

HUH? YOUR FAMILY OWNS A DOJO, ITO-SAN?

THIS IS REALLY A COINCID-ENCE!

ON THE OTHER HAND, I'M THE ONLY ONE SHE TOLD.

I SHOULDN'T BE, BUT I'M HAPPY ABOUT THAT.

OWW! YOU'LL REGRET THIS!

UM.. HELLO THERE.

SORRY FOR THE DELAY. LET'S GO IN.

TMP TMP

IS SHE YOUR GIRL-FRIEND?!

KA-BA SH

← A poke in the forehead

BIFF-BAM POW

Trying to figure out when to say hello.

...

YOU ARE, YOU HE-SHE!

WHO IS, YOU BRAT?!

OWW! MY BIG SISTER'S A MONSTER!

HUH?

THIS IS PRETTY RARE.

IT'S BEEN YEARS SINCE ITO BROUGHT HOME A FEMALE FRIEND.

NOT SINCE GRADE SCHOOL.

DRBBL DRBBL

YOUR GIRL-FRIEND?!

Playing with water

Twins

THEY'RE ALL THE SAME!

You'd better apologize, brothers!

SPSSSH

SORRY. I NEVER THOUGHT IT'D GET THAT FAR.

YOU'RE DRENCHING OUR GUEST!

RYUYA...

COULD YOU CLEAN YOUR CAR AT A CARWASH?

WHEN I CONFRONTED MY FATHER, THIS IS HOW IT TURNED OUT!

THE SON OF A DOJO OWNER BEING A FEMALE IMPERSONATOR.

SO YOU'RE A BAD SON?!

NO!

I'M THE ELDEST SON.

YOU SEE, I REALLY WANT TO BE AN ACTOR.

I'M THE ONLY SON IN A FAMILY OF DAUGHTERS.

WHEN I COME OF AGE, I WAS ALWAYS SUPPOSED TO INHERIT THE DOJO.

BUT...

THIS TENSION BETWEEN US LASTED A YEAR AND A HALF.

ALTHOUGH I WANTED MY INDEPENDENCE, MY FATHER WOULDN'T ALLOW IT.

JUST THE OPPOSITE, HE TRIED TO TIGHTEN HIS GRIP.

"...IF YOU REALLY WANT TO BE AN ACTOR..."

"...ON ONE CONDITION..."

...MY FATHER PUT ON THIS CONDITION...

WHEN HE FINALLY REALIZED I WAS SERIOUS...

WH--
WHAT ARE YOU SAYING? I CAN HELP!

I MEAN, WOULDN'T IT BE BETTER IF THERE WERE SOMEONE IN THE KNOW?

AND NOW, SOMEBODY FOUND OUT!

WHY IS MY HEART RACING?

B-BMP

B-BMP

B-BMP

B-BMP

AWWWW!

REALLY!

HE LOOKED LIKE A MAN JUST THEN!

FROM THAT MOMENT ON...

...

I'D LIKE TO GET TO KNOW YOU BETTER..

AND I...

I'M GOING TO BE JULIET?

BUT THE THING THAT MADE ME HAPPIEST...

...WAS HIS TRUST IN ME.

THE TWO OF US STARTED WORKING TOGETHER.

RELYING ON EACH OTHER.

THE SECRET WE SHARED DEEPENED OUR FRIENDSHIP.

YOU HAVE THE BEST CHEMISTRY WITH ITO-KUN. WILL YOU PLAY THE PART?

THAT'S RIGHT. I SAW YOU PRACTICE.

CHATTR

Start the Revolution!

REVOLUTIONARY GIRL UTENA:
THE ADOLESCENCE OF UTENA

Story and Art by Chiho Saito
Created by Be-PaPas

shôjo

On her very first day at Ohtori Academy, Utena Tenjou finds herself embroiled in sword duels, knotty romantic entanglement, and a string of shady alliances. There's a cloud of mystery hanging over the school's campus and everyone Utena meets harbors a dark and twisted secret.

A liberal adaptation of the movie by the same name, *THE ADOLESCENCE OF UTENA* veers wildly from its original source. More direct than the anime and more mature than the original manga series, this version of Chiho Saito's fractured fairy tale blasts Utena straight into the iconic stratosphere.

BASED ON THE MOVIE OF THE SAME NAME.

FROM THE CREATORS OF THE ORIGINAL REVOLUTIONARY GIRL UTENA MANGA SERIES.

● $9.95
● Available in October 2004

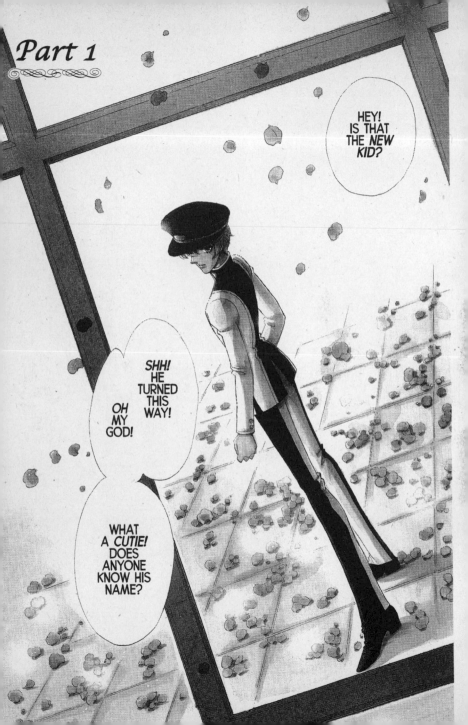

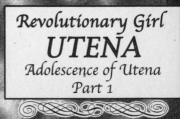

Revolutionary Girl
UTENA
Adolescence of Utena
Part 1

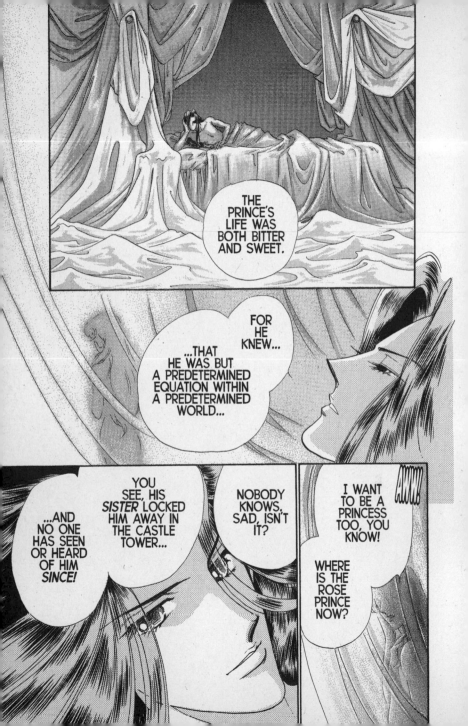

THERE'S MORE TO A PRINCE THAN *THAT*...

...MORE THAN YOU CAN EVEN IMAGINE...

SO YOU'RE *UTENA TENJOU*! LIKE IT HERE SO FAR?

I SURE DO!

EVERY-ONE'S SO *NICE* TO ME!

I WAS A BIT ANXIOUS AT FIRST... BUT I THINK I'LL FIT RIGHT IN.

I'M SO GLAD! I'M WAKABA SHINOHARA! WANT TO GO ON A TOUR OF THE CAMPUS? C'MON!

JUST STEP THIS WAY!

WE'LL START OVER HERE!

NO FAIR! DON'T HOG HIM!

55

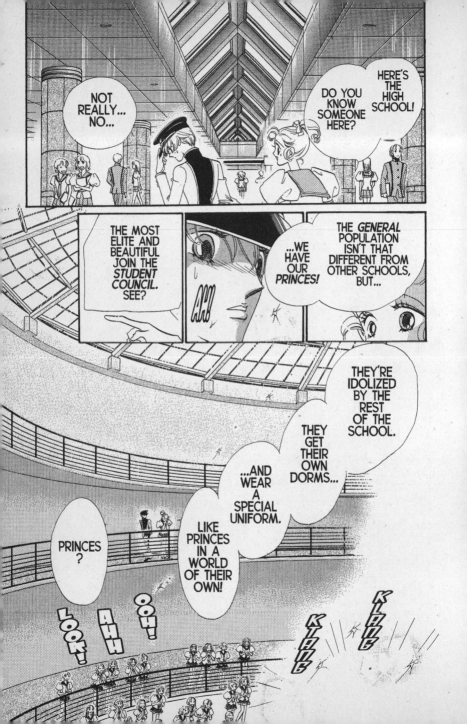

THE GIRL WITH THE CURLS...

...IS JURI ARISUGAWA...

...THE CAPTAIN OF THE FENCING TEAM.

SHE'S DUELING WITH MIKI KAORU...

...ALSO KNOWN AS *MICKEY.*

HE'S ONLY IN SEVENTH GRADE--BUT SO SMART THAT HE'S TAKING COLLEGE CLASSES ALREADY!

THERE'S ALSO SAIONJI, THE VICE PRESIDENT. AND OF COURSE, THE PRESIDENT...

...BUT I HEAR HIS TWIN SISTER MAKES IT HARD FOR HIM TO DATE.

THE GIRLS ALL THINK HE'S CUTE...

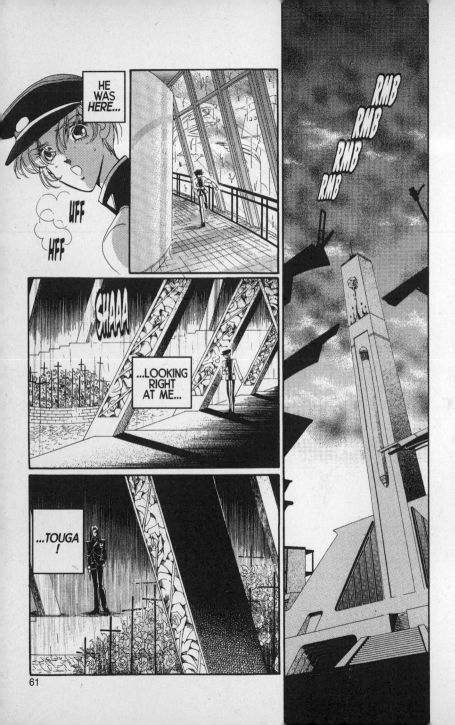

* This story is pure fiction. Any resemblance to real people, organizations or incidents is coincidental.

I WOULD JUST SAY SHE'S A BIT DREAMY.

THAT'S MEAN.

I'D SAY SHE'S UNSOPHIS- TICATED.

OR MAYBE THAT SHE'S MISSING A FEW SCREWS.

A HA HA HA HA!

LIKE THAT WARRIOR MOVIE WE SAW.

COOL. ♡

NORIKO'S MOVING TO HER DREAM WORLD TO BE A WARRIOR.

HEY, IF THOSE THEORIES ARE CORRECT...

NORIKO A WARRIOR?

GIVE ME A BREAK. SHE'S TOO SPACED OUT.

YOU GUYS. SAY WHAT- EVER YOU WANT.

A HA HA HA HA HA HA!

PLUS, SHE HAS NO SUPERNATURAL POWER. SHE'S JUST AN ORDINARY HIGH SCHOOL GIRL. MAYBE SHE COULD BE THE SIDEKICK.

WHEN I WAS CHATTING WITH MY GIRL- FRIENDS...

I HAD NO IDEA WHAT WAS GOING TO...

73

I'M
DREAM-
ING.

I'M
SLEEPING
IN MY SOFT
COMFORTER
RIGHT
NOW.

BLOOD
RED.

Mur Mur

LOOK
AT THE
WATER.

I
SEE.

THIS
IS A
DREAM.

THE
WATER
HAS
TURNED
...

IT'S
THE
AWAKEN-
ING.

HERE IS GREENWOOD

Story and Art by Yukie Nasu

shôjo

STEP INSIDE THE WALLS OF GREENWOOD... IF YOU DARE.

If 15-year-old Kazuya Hasukawa's stomach wasn't perforated in a car accident, it would have been perforated by an ulcer! The woman he loves just married his older brother, and worse, he is bringing her home to live with them! Kazuya is forced out of the house, and the only option is to enter the exclusive all-male boarding school, Ryokuto Academy, more popularly known as "Greenwood." But the car accident laid Kazuya up for quite some time, so he missed a month of school! And because Kazuya arrived at school late, he is introduced to his new roommate in the last available room—Shun Kisaragi, the cutest girl in the guy's dorm!

Here is Greenwood

story and art by Yukie Nasu vol.1

FROM THE CREATOR OF "FLOWER DESTROYER" AND "DARK AGE."

AN 11-VOLUME MANGA SERIES THAT HAS SPAWNED AN OAV, DVD, AND POPULAR CD SOUNDTRACK.

- Bimonthly
- $9.99
- Available in October 2004

RATED T FOR TEEN

... WAS THE SCHOOL'S PRINCIPAL.

... THE OLD GUY WHO ADMINISTERED MY ENTRANCE EXAM ...

BUT THE TEST OF YOUR CHARACTER IS JUST BEGINNING.

THANK YOU, SIR.

... WILL SERVE AS A HUGE DISADVANTAGE FOR YOU.

BEING OUT THAT ENTIRE MONTH ...

THE FIRST MONTH OF A NEW HIGH-SCHOOL STUDENT'S LIFE IS CRUCIAL.

I NEVER KNEW ...

A BLIZZARD DISRUPTED DRIVERS' VISION AND MADE THE ROADS HAZARDOUS ON MY WAY TO TAKE THE EXAM.

YES, SIR.

THE LETTER INFORMING ME WHETHER I PASSED OR FAILED WAS A CASUALTY OF AN ACCIDENT WITH THE MAIL TRUCK.

DO YOUR BEST, SON !

BUT I MUST ASK YOU, HASUKAWA, TO OVERCOME THAT HANDICAP.

KNOCK KNOCK

BUT I NO LONGER HAD A HOME TO GO BACK TO.

THAT'S HOW I CAME TO REALIZE THAT THE CLOSER I GOT TO THIS SCHOOL, THE MORE THE DEVIL HAD IT IN FOR ME.

AND JUST AS I WAS COMING TO SURVEY THE SCHOOL, A CAR RACING NEAR THE FRONT GATE NEARLY HIT ME.

COME IN.

I WON'T LET THEM BEAT ME!

AND THIS IS YOUR DORM'S HEAD RESIDENT, MITSURU IKEDA.

THIS IS THE STUDENT BODY PRESIDENT, SHINOBU TEZUKA.

ALLOW ME TO INTRODUCE YOU.

EXCUSE US.

...SO YOU CAN ASK THEM ANYTHING. THINK OF THEM AS OLDER BROTHERS.

THEY ARE SEMPAI AT YOUR DORM...

WE'LL LEAD YOU TO THE DORM.

LIKEWISE.

NICE TO MEET YOU BOTH.

I LEAVE THIS YOUNG MAN IN YOUR HANDS.

YES, SIR.

OLDER... BROTHERS...?

WERE THEY ELECTED BASED ON THEIR LOOKS?

IT HAS ALWAYS BEEN MY DREAM TO GO TO ROKUTO ACADEMY, THE SCHOOL WHERE MY OLDER BROTHER STUDIED.

SHALL WE GO, HASU-KAWA?

EXCUSE US.

AND KAZUHIRO WAS MY IDEAL MAN.

HE WAS A ROLE MODEL FOR THE WHOLE COMMUNITY.

THE ONE WHO HAS TAKEN CARE OF ME, ALL BY HIMSELF, SINCE OUR PARENTS DIED IN ACCIDENTS.

...WHEN HIS ENTIRE ATTITUDE SUDDENLY LIGHTENED.

HE WAS ABOUT TO GRADUATE FROM COLLEGE...

EH?

AND A YOUNG MAN'S IDEAL CRUMBLED INTO DUST.

I'LL NEVER FORGIVE HIM!

WHAT? KAZUHIRO, WHAT KIND OF WORK DID YOU SAY YOU GOT?

IT MUST HAVE BEEN A ROYAL PAIN FOR YOU TO BE HOSPITALIZED JUST BEFORE ENTERING SCHOOL.

WERE YOU HURT BADLY?

YES, YOU COULD SAY THAT.

DID YOU SAY SOMETHING?

AH! NO.

YEAH...
...SORRY IF IT UPSET YOU.

IT'S GREAT TO SEE YOU ALL BETTER NOW.

I SEE.

GRIN

↑ Too many words for the balloon.

KACHAK

IS SOMETHING WRONG, HASU-KAWA?

SMILE..

SHUN KISARAGI.

...YOUR ROOM-MATE.

OH, THAT.

210

I THOUGHT ... I SAW A GIRL IN MY ROOM.

THIS IS ...

SHE IS A GIRL.

H-HOLD IT!!

KACHIK

O--OH! YOU SURPRISED ME! I THOUGHT YOU WERE A GIRL!

SMILE

103

106

HASU-
KAWA
!

HASU-
KAWA
!

POIT

MM
...

I'M
CHANGING
AT
THE
MOMENT.

ARE YOU
AWAKE?
CAN YOU
STAY
COVERED
UP FOR A
WHILE
LONGER?

食器返却口

Cafeteria

WITH NO
OTHER
CHOICE, I
FINALLY
FELL
ASLEEP.

.....

I'M
FINISHED
!
♥

GOOD
MORNING,
HASU-
KAWA.

FEED
ME!

OH,
G'MORNING.

Living Dead

YEAH
...

YOU'RE
GOING
TO
SCHOOL
TODAY,
RIGHT?

UM
...

DID
YOU
SLEEP
WELL
LAST
NIGHT
?

THAT'S
RIGHT
!

OKAY
...

TO BE
HONEST, I
DOUBT THEY'LL
GO EASY ON
YOU, BUT IF
YOU HAVE ANY
PROBLEMS, YOU
CAN BRING
THEM TO US.

CLASSES
WILL BE A
PROBLEM.

IT'S TOO BAD WE'RE NOT IN THE SAME CLASSES.

THAT LOOK JUST ISN'T HER!

THIS IS NO TIME FOR A MELT DOWN!

PII PII PII PII

I CAN'T WORRY ABOUT THIS! I HAVE A MONTH'S WORTH OF SCHOOL WORK I HAVE TO MAKE UP!

May, when there aren't many birds...

YOU KNOW ABOUT THAT?

HASU-KAWA!

I'M SO LOST!

I ASSUMED AS MUCH.

KISARAGI'S POPULAR!

I HEAR YOU'RE ROOMING WITH KISARAGI!

BUT DON'T LET IT RUIN YOU!

DON'T FOLLOW THE PATH TO HELL!

I KNOW THAT GREENWOOD IS A HAVEN OF WEIRDOES!

FATE PUNKED YOU!

WELL, HANG IN THERE!

GRMP

Men's Room

I DON'T KNOW HOW, BUT...

I DID THAT.

I KILLED THEM.

THAT'S WHAT I BELIEVE.

SOMEWHERE INSIDE ME IS A TERRIBLE POWER...

AND IT'S AN INFERNO.

WHY DID THEY ACT LIKE THEY KNOW EVERYTHING?

WHO... WHAT... ARE THOSE PEOPLE?

IF YOU KNOW YOUR POWER...

CREEPY.

Pi Pi Pi PIZZA

PLEASE DROP BY.

WELCOME!

OZEKI!?

THAT'S A LOSER NAME.

UM...

I'M MICHIRU OZEKI.

I'M KUROSU.

AND YOU ARE?

AH, YES. THE BUS GIRL.

SO YOU'VE COME.

Yokozuna is the highest rank in sumo; ozeki is the second highest. —PD

OF PSYCHIC POWER, OF COURSE!

You're too loud and not making sense.

OF WHAT?

WELL I'M A YOKOZUNA— A CHAMPION!

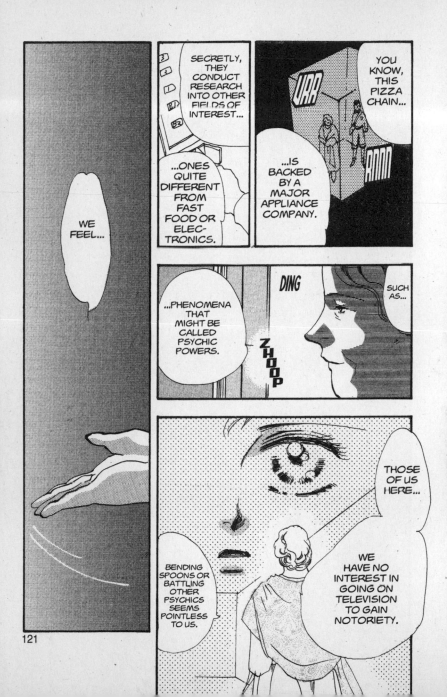

WE FEEL...

SECRETLY, THEY CONDUCT RESEARCH INTO OTHER FIELDS OF INTEREST...

...ONES QUITE DIFFERENT FROM FAST FOOD OR ELECTRONICS.

YOU KNOW, THIS PIZZA CHAIN...

...IS BACKED BY A MAJOR APPLIANCE COMPANY.

...PHENOMENA THAT MIGHT BE CALLED PSYCHIC POWERS.

DING

ZHOOP

SUCH AS...

THOSE OF US HERE...

WE HAVE NO INTEREST IN GOING ON TELEVISION TO GAIN NOTORIETY.

BENDING SPOONS OR BATTLING OTHER PSYCHICS SEEMS POINTLESS TO US.

I CAN'T DO THAT.

I...

I CAN'T.

WHOA!

FOOM!

Pizza oven

I FEEL SICK...

WHAT!?

THAT'S PATHETIC.

YOU MEAN YOU CAN'T CONTROL IT!?

ROOKIE!

NOT HIM AGAIN!

I DIDN'T DO ANYTHING!

THIS GUY REALLY BUGS ME...

HEY, OZEKI, WHADJA DO?

FIRE JUST SHOT OUT OF THE OVEN.

...SEEMS TO BE BASED ON A FALSE ASSUMPTION.

Yes...?

UM... MOST OF WHAT YOU'VE BEEN SAYING...

AN ENORMOUS WALL OF ROCK HAS COLLAPSED ONTO THE HIGHWAY.

BATA BATA BATA

AN EMERGENCY TEAM HAS BEEN DISPATCHED TO THE SCENE...

ALTHOUGH THEIR STRATEGY IS REPORTEDLY STILL BEING DEBATED.

WEEOOO!!

WEEOOO!!

WAA WAA

A NUMBER OF VEHICLES APPEAR TO HAVE BEEN STRUCK.

IT IS STILL UNKNOWN IF THERE ARE ANY SURVIVORS—

HEY!

IT'S A MIRA-CLE!

WOO! YAY! HOO!

FEEOOO FEEOOO

I'M AFRAID!

THERE ARE FIVE SURVIVORS! MEDICAL CREWS ARE RUSHING TO AID THEM!

DID WE SAVE ALL OF 'EM, I WONDER?

WHOA! OH!

YUP, WE JUST MADE IT.

YOU SEE...

...FOR A LITTLE WHILE AFTER HE USES HIS POWERS...

MY LEG...

NH!

...PARTS OF HIS BODY STOP WORKING.

WELL, WHICH IS IT, AMANO? YOUR EYE OR YOUR LEG?

MY EYE...

134

action

ac•tion (ak′shən) *n.* **1.** To initiate or proceed. **2.** A responsibility, mission, or duty. **3.** To move or advance toward change, as in an attempt to better a situation or environment. **4.** A call to battle between good and evil.

Action titles from VIZ:

Wolf's Rain • No Need For Tenchi!

WHY SHOULD WE HAVE TO HIDE WHO WE ARE...

ALL I'M DOING, IS USING THEIR IGNORANCE...

...TO MY ADVANTAGE.

...THESE RULES ARE VILE.

TSUME
...

WHO'S
THAT!?

THWP

ARE
YOU
OKAY,
TSUME
...

DON'T
TOUCH
ME.

YOU--

YOU'RE
BLEED-
ING.

...I
...THOUGHT
THAT
MAYBE YOU
DIDN'T CARE
WHEN ONE
OF YOUR
FRIENDS
DIED...

THA--
...
THANKS
FOR
...
SAVING
ME...

...
WE'RE
NOT
FRIENDS.

WHAT?

...there's no such thing...as paradise

so...what is...this yearning...stirring in me?!

Kallak

WHIMPER

...THE FIRST THING THAT CAUSED CHEZA TO REACT...

WAS *WOLF'S BLOOD*...

...APPARENTLY.

146

CHEZA HERSELF IS THE CROWNING ACHIEVEMENT OF AN ALCHEMY THAT IS UNPROVABLE.

THE FLOWER MAIDEN ...

AND THE WOLVES ...

ARE BEING DRAWN TO EACH OTHER ...

IT'S EXACTLY THE SORT OF THING...

THOSE ANCIENT SCHOLARS WOULD COME UP WITH...

152

...A WOLF.

...HEY...

ARE YOU ALIVE...?

154

YAWWWWWN

WAAH

GUESS NO ONE CAN HALT THE WORK OF A *GENIUS!*

AHHH!

GOT TOO CARRIED AWAY WITH MY RESEARCH LAST NIGHT-- DIDN'T SLEEP A *WINK!*

WHATCHA DOIN'?

THIS TAKES *HEAVY* CONCEN-TRATION!

KEEP IT DOWN, WASHU!

I SENT THEM AWAY! THEY'RE VISITING THE OLD MAN!

WHERE ARE ALL THE **NORMAL** PEOPLE?

WHAT A **DORK**!

SO BE QUIET, ALL RIGHT?

SPSS
SPPSS

JUST THIRTY-THREE COINS TO GO 'TIL I REACH TEN THOUSAND!

TUP

FLUP

GREAT.

UH-OH...

WELL, I COULD USE SOME EXCITEMENT!

HMPH!!

OH, HELLO THERE, MS. WASHU.

NOOOOO!

WHA'S UP?

JUST ENJOYING SOME R&R...

EVER SINCE THE KAGATO INCIDENT, YOU TWO ARE GROWIN' **ROOTS**!

PLEASE, SASAMI! I'LL GIVE YOU THAT BRACELET YOU'VE ALWAYS WANTED.

YOU CAN PRACTICE THE RECIPE I SHOWED YOU EARLIER!

WON'T THAT BE FUN?!

I'VE GOT A GREAT IDEA! SASAMI, WHY DON'T YOU TEACH HER HOW TO MAKE IT?

YOU *CLUTCH-PIG!* IT'S A DEAL!

OF COURSE! YOU'RE A *BIG* GIRL!

AND THE MATCHING NECK-LACE?

DO YOU REALLY THINK I CAN DO IT, AYEKA?

?

THE NUMBER ONE RULE IN SPICING THIS DISH IS *NEVER* TO USE TOO MUCH SUGAR. IF YOU USE TOO MUCH SUGAR AT FIRST, YOU'LL NEED MORE SOY SAUCE TO BALANCE THE FLAVOR... BLAH...BLAH...BLABLABLAH...

THE LOTUS ROOTS AND CARROTS SHOULD BE CUT INTO ROUND SLICES. BURDOCKS SHOULD BE DIVIDED INTO FOUR PIECES VERTICALLY. THE KONNYAKU PASTE SHOULD BE CUT IN TWO WAYS (ONE TWISTED IN THE MIDDLE), AND THE CHICKEN SHOULD BE IN CHUNKS OF DIFFERENT SIZES. THEN COMES THE FLAVORING!

YES, YES! GO ON!

THE TRICK IS TO CUT THE INGREDIENTS IN *JUST* THE RIGHT WAY!

TH-THAT *HORRIBLE* VOICE! IT MUST BE...

UNLIKE *OTHER* PRINCESSES WE KNOW!

TEE HEE HEE

OH, SASAMI! YOU ARE *SO* SMART!

SHOULD'VE KNOWN...

YUP!

169

172

editor's choice

ed•i•tor's choice (ed´i-tôrs chois) n. **1.** That which defines cutting-edge. **2.** Manga known for its daring, creativity, and artistry. **3.** Manga that sets the standard for excellence and reveals its promise.

Editor's Choice titles from VIZ:

Tough

THE NADASHINKAGE STYLE!?*

Chapter 4: The Fateful Handshake

*NADA = ANCIENT OSAKA, SHINKAGE = GOD SHADOW--ED.

J-JUST WHO ARE YOU, ANYWAY?

HUH? HOW'D YOU KNOW THAT?

BUT WHEN IT COMES TO GOOD LOOKS AND FIGHTING, THAT KURODA'S GOT NOTHIN' ON ME!

I MAY NOT BE RICH... OR... SMART...

WE'RE DESTINED TO BE TOGETHER.

AHHH... TAKAKO KAWASHIMA! ♡

HUH?

KIIBO, WHAT'S THIS NADA-SHINKA-WHAT-EVER KURODA MENTIONED?

H-HE WAS?

BRUCE LEE WAS INTO IT JUST BEFORE HE DIED.

IT'S A CURSED MARTIAL ART THAT COMES FROM ANCIENT CHINA. WHOEVER STUDIES IT DIES WITHIN THREE YEARS.

HEY! KIIBO!

YOSHIMOTO SHINKIGEKI* IS ON TONIGHT.

LET'S GO HOME AND WATCH TV.

PSYCH! NOT REALLY...

Bwah ha!

MARUTA

*A POPULAR KANSAI TROUPE OF STAND-UP COMICS AND STORYTELLERS -- ED.

EVERYTHING HE THREW AT YOU WAS POTENTIALLY LETHAL...
IF THE FIGHT HAD GONE ON, IT WOULD'VE GOTTEN UGLY.
HE WOULD'VE GIVEN YOU A REAL FIGHT.
AND...
HEH

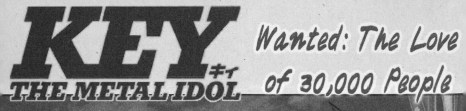

COMPLETE OUR SURVEY AND LET US KNOW WHAT YOU THINK!

☐ Please do NOT send me information about VIZ products, news and events, special offers, or other information.

☐ Please do NOT send me information from VIZ's trusted business partners.

Name: _____

Address: _____

City: _____ **State:** _____ **Zip:** _____

E-mail: _____

☐ Male ☐ Female **Date of Birth** (mm/dd/yyyy): ___/___/___ (Under 13? Parental consent required)

What race/ethnicity do you consider yourself? (please check one)

☐ Asian/Pacific Islander ☐ Black/African American ☐ Hispanic/Latino

☐ Native American/Alaskan Native ☐ White/Caucasian ☐ Other: _____

What VIZ product did you purchase? (check all that apply and indicate title purchased)

☐ DVD/VHS _____

☐ Graphic Novel _____

☐ Magazines _____

☐ Merchandise _____

Reason for purchase: (check all that apply)

☐ Special offer ☐ Favorite title ☐ Gift

☐ Recommendation ☐ Other _____

Where did you make your purchase? (please check one)

☐ Comic store ☐ Bookstore ☐ Mass/Grocery Store

☐ Newsstand ☐ Video/Video Game Store ☐ Other: _____

☐ Online (site: _____)

What other VIZ properties have you purchased/own? _____

_____

How many anime and/or manga titles have you purchased in the last year? How many were VIZ titles? (please check one from each column)

ANIME

☐ None
☐ 1-4
☐ 5-10
☐ 11+

MANGA

☐ None
☐ 1-4
☐ 5-10
☐ 11+

VIZ

☐ None
☐ 1-4
☐ 5-10
☐ 11+

I find the pricing of VIZ products to be: (please check one)

☐ Cheap   ☐ Reasonable   ☐ Expensive

What genre of manga and anime would you like to see from VIZ? (please check two)

☐ Adventure   ☐ Comic Strip   ☐ Science Fiction   ☐ Fighting
☐ Horror   ☐ Romance   ☐ Fantasy   ☐ Sports

What do you think of VIZ's new look?

☐ Love It   ☐ It's OK   ☐ Hate It   ☐ Didn't Notice   ☐ No Opinion

Which do you prefer? (please check one)

☐ Reading right-to-left
☐ Reading left-to-right

Which do you prefer? (please check one)

☐ Sound effects in English
☐ Sound effects in Japanese with English captions
☐ Sound effects in Japanese only with a glossary at the back

THANK YOU! Please send the completed form to:

VIZ Survey
42 Catharine St.
Poughkeepsie, NY 12601

All information provided will be used for internal purposes only. We promise not to sell or otherwise divulge your information.